Collection Edits by **JUSTIN EISINGER** and **ALONZO SIMON**

Collection Design by **JEFF POWELL**

Production Assistance by **GILBERTO LAZCANO**

Special thanks to Joan Hilty, Linda Lee, and Kat van Dam for their invaluable assistance.

ISBN: 978-1-63140-590-7

18 17 16 15   1 2 3 4

IDW®

www.IDWPUBLISHING.com

IDW founded by Ted Adams, Alex Garner, Kris Oprisko, and Robbie Robbins

Ted Adams, CEO & Publisher
Greg Goldstein, President & COO
Robbie Robbins, EVP/Sr. Graphic Artist
Chris Ryall, Chief Creative Officer/Editor-in-Chief
Matthew Ruzicka, CPA, Chief Financial Officer
Alan Payne, VP of Sales
Dirk Wood, VP of Marketing
Lorelei Bunjes, VP of Digital Services
Jeff Webber, VP of Digital Publishing & Business Development

Facebook: **facebook.com/idwpublishing**
Twitter: **@idwpublishing**
YouTube: **youtube.com/idwpublishing**
Tumblr: **tumblr.idwpublishing.com**
Instagram: **instagram.com/idwpublishing**

Originally published as TEENAGE MUTANT NINJA TURTLES/GHOSTBUSTERS issues #1-4.

TEENAGE MUTANT NINJA TURTLES GHOSTBUSTERS

STORY	**ERIK BURNHAM & TOM WALTZ**
ART	**DAN SCHOENING**
ADDITIONAL ART	**CHARLES PAUL WILSON III & CORY SMITH** (CH. 1)
COLORS	**LUIS ANTONIO DELGADO**
ADDITIONAL COLORS	**RONDA PATTISON** (CH. 1)
LETTERS	**NEIL UYETAKE**
SERIES EDITS	**BOBBY CURNOW**
COVER ART	**DAN SCHOENING**
COVER COLORS	**LUIS ANTONIO DELGADO**

DRAMATIS

DR. PETER VENKMAN
Ph.D. in parapsychology and psychology. Innate ability to manipulate. Generally considered the mouth of the Ghostbusters.

DR. EGON SPENGLER
Ph.D. in parapsychology. Polymath. Occasionally accused of having Asperger's, but he's really just not usually interested in what you have to say.

DR. RAY STANTZ
Ph.D. in parapsychology. Tinkerer and inventor. Co-designed all of the Ghostbusting equipment. Takes joy in discovery. The heart of the team.

WINSTON ZEDDEMORE
Honorary doctorate. In night school for law. Marine. Soft spot for kids and hard luck cases. A believer.

JANINE MELNITZ
Office manager and occasional Ghostbuster. A little bit psychic about certain things. Not to be trifled with.

KYLIE GRIFFIN
Manages Ray's Occult Bookstore. Fantastic researcher. Eidetic memory. Lack of patience. Likes ghostbusting more than she lets on.

PERSONAE

MICHELANGELO
Friendliest and most outgoing of the Ninja Turtles, Mikey loves meeting people.

LEONARDO
The leader of the Turtles, the most focused, and the most spiritually attuned.

DONATELLO
Smartest of the Turtles, able to understand and work with complex technologies.

RAPHAEL
The most temperamental of the Turtles, a born brawler.

APRIL O'NEIL
Science whiz, friend to the Turtles, aided in the construction of the dimensional transport.

CASEY JONES
Hockey-loving vigilante, and friend to the Turtles.

HAROLD LILLJA
Scientist and colleague of Donatello, aided in the construction of the dimensional transport.

KITSUNE
An immortal playing a game for control of the Turtles' Earth. Closely aligned with the Foot Clan. (See "TMNT: Secret History of the Foot Clan")

KRANG
Extradimensional Warlord who deals with Kitsune in the distant past. Uses portal technology to cross to Earth.

CHI-YOU
An immortal playing a game for control of the (Turtles') Earth. Worshipped as a war god in China.

1

CROSSING THE DIVIDE

ART BY **DAN SCHOENING** COLORS BY **LUIS ANTONIO DELGADO**

THOUSANDS OF YEARS AGO, POWERFUL IMMORTALS RULED THE EARTH.

THEN THEY MYSTERIOUSLY DISAPPEARED.

FOR A TIME, THEY INSPIRED MYTH AND LEGEND... BUT ULTIMATELY FADED FROM MEMORY.

LOST TO HISTORY AND BELIEVED BY MOST TO HAVE NEVER REALLY EXISTED AT ALL...

...NEVER TO RETURN AGAIN.

BUT, REALLY, WHAT DOES "NEVER" MEAN TO AN IMMORTAL?

YOU CONSPIRE WITH *DEMONS!* A *CLEAR BREACH* OF THE RULES!

YOU WERE TO ONLY USE *MORTALS* AS PAWNS, SISTER! YOU FORFEIT YOUR PLACE IN THE GAME... AND YOUR *SOUL!*

TEMPER TEMPER, CHI-YOU. I AM STILL PLAYING TO THE *SPIRIT* OF THE RULES, IF NOT TO THE EXACT *LETTER.*

AND STILL YOU SEEM SET ON PUNISHING ME. PITY YOU AREN'T FAST ENOUGH TO DO SO.

YOU CAN'T DODGE FOREVER.

WE'RE *IMMORTAL*, DEAR BROTHER OF *COURSE* I COULD.

BUT YOU'RE RIGHT.

THAT *WOULD* GET BORING.

WHAT—

MIKEY, DO YOU HAVE ANY IDEA WHAT THE FLOATING GUY IS YELLING ABOUT?
BEATS ME, DUDE. WHATEVER IT IS HE'S SPEAKING, IT'S **NOT** JAPANESE.
OH, FOR—
—HOW 'BOUT WE TAKE CARE OF THIS GUY INSTEAD OF STANDIN' AROUND, DEBATIN'?
HEADS UP, FLATTOP!
<EH?? A DEMON?>
WHAT THE—

ART BY **KEVIN EASTMAN** COLORS BY **RONDA PATTISON**

2

THE MEETING OF THE MINDS

ART BY **DAN SCHOENING** COLORS BY **LUIS ANTONIO DELGADO**

ART BY **SHANNON RITCHIE** COLORS BY **PARIS ALLEYNE**

3

SHOWDOWN IN CHINATOWN

ART BY **DAN SCHOENING** COLORS BY **LUIS ANTONIO DELGADO**

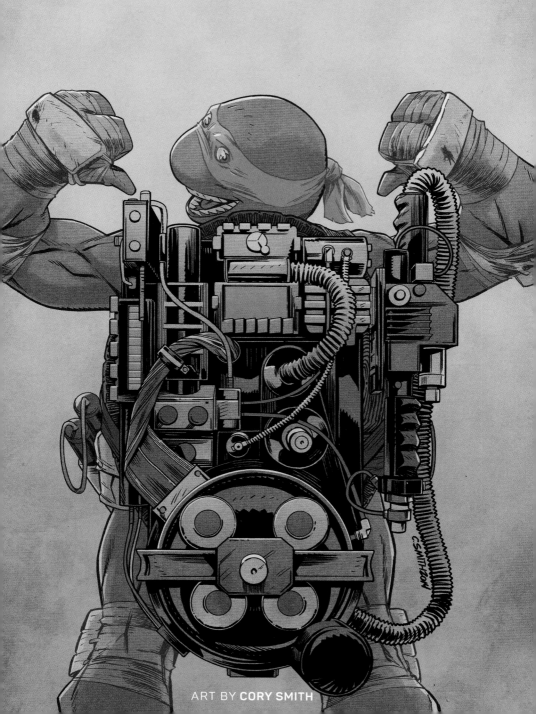

4

THE LONG GOODBYE

ART BY DAN SCHOENING COLORS BY LUIS ANTONIO DELGADO

THE FIREHOUSE.

IT'S BEEN HOURS SINCE THE DISPERSAL OF CHI-YOU'S SPECTRAL FORM, AND OUR HEROES HAVE BEEN *BUSY.*

EGON SPENGLER AND DONATELLO HAVE MADE STRIDES TOWARDS RECREATING A FUNCTIONING INTERSPATIAL TELEPORTATION UNIT.

OH MAN, EGON, YOU HAVE STUFF HERE I'D HAVE TO *INVENT* BACK HOME. I THINK WE'RE GONNA MAKE IT.

UH, BARRING *CATASTROPHE,* OF COURSE.

OF COURSE.

OKAY, HOW'S THAT LOOKING?

CONNECTED ON THE FIRST TRY! APRIL, YOU HAVE A GIFT FOR THIS. WHATEVER YOUR MAJOR IS, I'D CHANGE IT TO ENGINEERING.

CALM DOWN, BOSS.

RAY STANTZ, APRIL O'NEIL, AND KYLIE GRIFFIN CONTINUE WORK ON A DEVICE TO FREE CHI-YOU'S THRALLS FROM HIS CONTROL.

AS FOR THE LESS TECHNOLOGICALLY GIFTED... THEY CAN ONLY WAIT.

MAN, THE BALANCE ON THIS IS PERFECT.

SEE? NO ONE *EVER* APPRECIATES THAT!

CHECK IT OUT, I *TOLD* YOU GUYS THESE THINGS WOULD STRETCH!

KLANGKLANGKLANGKLANGKLANGKLANG

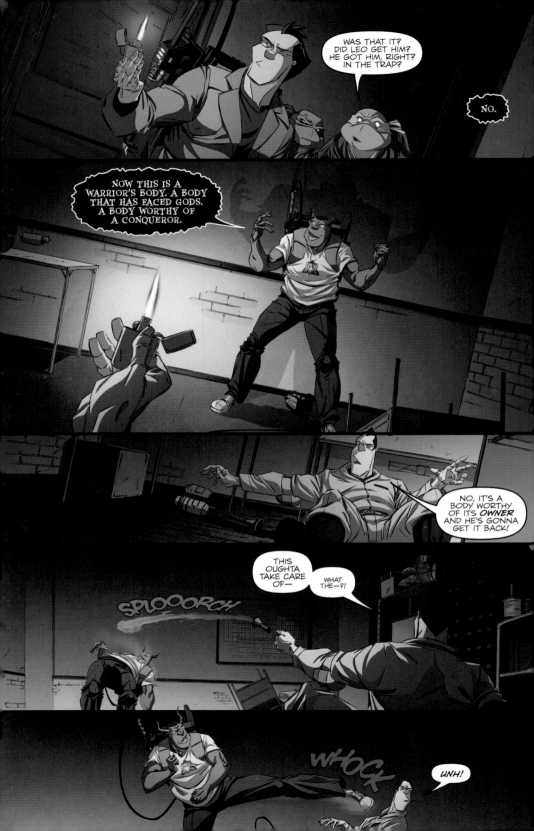

ART BY **ROBERT ATKINS** COLORS BY **SIMON GOUGH**

ART BY BRENT PEEPLES

ART BY OZZY FERNANDEZ & TONY KORDOS

ART BY ADAM GORHAM
COLORS BY PARIS ALLEY

ART BY JERRY GAYLORD

ART BY **MATT SLAY**

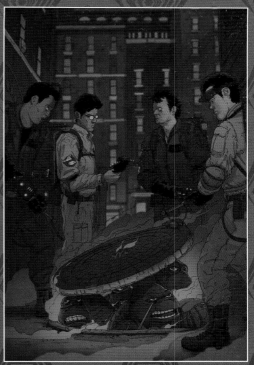

ART BY **TRISTAN JONES**

ART BY **ADAM GORHAM**

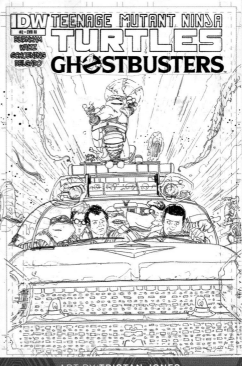

ART BY **TRISTAN JONES**

ART BY BRENT PEEPLES
COLORS BY RONDA PATTISON

ART BY ADAM GORHAM

ART BY BRENT PEEPLES
COLORS BY LUIS ANTONIO DELGADO

ART BY ADAM GORHAM